The Thinking Tree

BOOK OF
STATE BIRDS

Nature Study Handbook

Learning ornithology for the official
state birds in all **50 US** States;
locating their scientific names,
research projects, creative
activities, and more!

WRITTEN AND DESIGNED BY:
NORA McCAIN APPLE

Illustrations/Artwork by: Anna Kidalova
Cover Artwork by: Sarah Janisse Brown

FunSchooling.com

THE THINKING TREE, LLC

My name is: _____

_____

Date: _____

Age: _____

Instructions:

Ornithology is a branch of zoology (the study of animals) which specializes in the bird species. The word *ornithology* is a Latin word which means "bird science." A scientist that specializes in the study of birds is called an *ornithologist*.

Humans began studying animals as far back as Adam and Eve. It was necessary to identify which animals were able to be used for food or be domesticated. Today, ornithologists study approximately **18,000** different species of birds!

This workbook will include science, geography, history, language arts, and creative arts all in one! If you are using the book for school, work on one page a day, or as many as you want to fit into your curriculum. The vocabulary words are located at the beginning so you will understand the terms when you research each state bird.

This is a workbook purposed to develop research skills. Think of all the different ways to research the bird species. Use a dictionary in book form to look up and learn the vocabulary words. Have your parent help with any searches on the Internet or schedule a library day to research the information. Choose your favorite reading spot, such as a beanbag chair, comfy desk, or under your favorite oak tree. Be sure to have colored pencils, pens, or markers ready to doodle and practice your art skills!

I know you will have fun learning about our amazing botanical earth!

UNITED STATES OF AMERICA

Find and color your state!

What State do you live in? _____

Here are some helpful websites for your parents to help with your research:

- https://www.50states.com/bird/
- https://state.1keydata.com/state-birds.php
- https://statesymbolsusa.org/categories/bird
- https://www.officialusa.com/info/category/state-birds/
- https://en.wikipedia.org/wiki/List_of_U.S._state_birds
- https://en.wikipedia.org/wiki/List_of_endangered_birds

VOCABULARY WORDS

(class) Aves: _____

_____
_____

binomial nomenclature: _____

_____
_____

carnivore: _____

_____
_____

conservation: _____

_____
_____

domesticate: _____

_____
_____

ecology: _____

_____
_____

guano: _____

_____
_____

habitat: _____

_____
_____

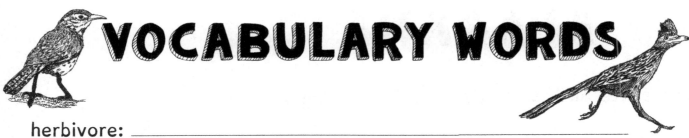

VOCABULARY WORDS

herbivore: _____
_____
_____

migrate: _____
_____
_____

molt: _____
_____
_____

omnivore: _____
_____
_____

ornithology: _____
_____
_____

oviparous: _____
_____
_____

poultry: _____
_____
_____

zoology: _____
_____

ALABAMA

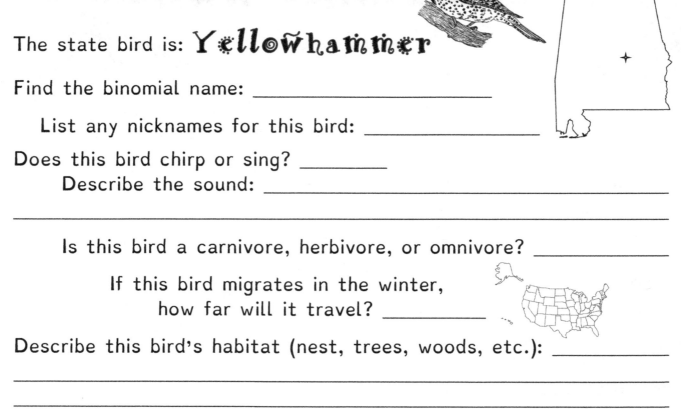

The state bird is: Yellowhammer

Find the binomial name: _____

List any nicknames for this bird: _____

Does this bird chirp or sing? _____
Describe the sound: _____
_____

Is this bird a carnivore, herbivore, or omnivore? _____

If this bird migrates in the winter,
how far will it travel? _____

Describe this bird's habitat (nest, trees, woods, etc.): _____
_____
_____
_____

Eurasian Yellowhammer

List the different colors of this bird:

Males: _____

_____

Females: _____

_____

Find this state on page 5 and use a different color to fill it in.

CREATIVE WRITING

In the space below, write a poem, short story, or a unique history tid-bit about the state bird. If this bird lives in your state, try taking a picture of the bird in its natural habitat and tape the picture to this page!

_____

_____

_____

_____

_____

_____

_____

_____

_____

_____

What is the bird's average wingspan?

_____

What is the average weight?

_____

Which region did this bird originate?

_____

Can this bird be domesticated?

_____

List the sources you used to research this bird:

Books: _____

_____

Websites: _____

Other sources: _____

_____

ALASKA

The state bird is: **Willow Ptarmigan**

Find the binomial name: _____

   List any nicknames for this bird: _____

Does this bird chirp or sing? _____

   Describe the sound: _____

_____

   Is this bird a carnivore, herbivore, or omnivore? _____

   If this bird migrates in the winter,
      how far will it travel? _____

Describe this bird's habitat (nest, trees, woods, etc.): _____

_____

_____

_____

Fun fact:
The Willow Ptarmigan
has feathered toes!

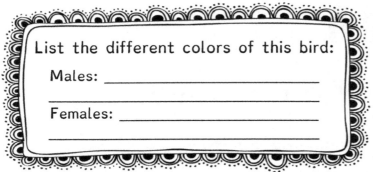
List the different colors of this bird:

Males: _____

_____

Females: _____

_____

Find this state on page 5 and use a different color to fill it in.

****

CREATIVE WRITING

In the space below, write a poem, short story, or a unique history tid-bit about the state bird. If this bird lives in your state, try taking a picture of the bird in its natural habitat and tape the picture to this page!

_____

_____

_____

_____

_____

_____

_____

_____

****

What is the bird's average wingspan?

_____

What is the average weight?

_____

Which region did this bird originate?

_____

Can this bird be domesticated?

_____

List the sources you used to research this bird:

Books: _____

_____

Websites: _____

_____

Other sources: _____

_____

ARIZONA

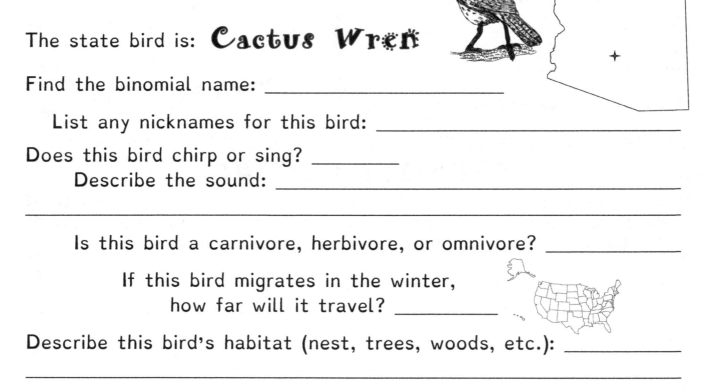

The state bird is: *Cactus Wren*

Find the binomial name: _____

   List any nicknames for this bird: _____

Does this bird chirp or sing? _____
     Describe the sound: _____
_____

    Is this bird a carnivore, herbivore, or omnivore? _____

     If this bird migrates in the winter,
       how far will it travel? _____

Describe this bird's habitat (nest, trees, woods, etc.): _____
_____
_____
_____

Fun fact:
The cactus wren acquires most of its necessary water from food, enabling it to live happily in the desert!

12

List the different colors of this bird:

Males: _____

_____

Females: _____

_____

Find this state on page **5** and use a different color to fill it in.

****

CREATIVE WRITING

In the space below, write a poem, short story, or a unique history tid-bit about the state bird. If this bird lives in your state, try taking a picture of the bird in its natural habitat and tape the picture to this page!

_____

_____

_____

_____

_____

_____

_____

_____

_____

****

What is the bird's average wingspan?

_____

What is the average weight?

Which region did this bird originate?

_____

Can this bird be domesticated?

_____

List the sources you used to research this bird:

Books: _____

Websites: _____

Other sources: _____

_____

ARKANSAS

The state bird is:

Northern Mockingbird

Find the binomial name: _____

List any nicknames for this bird: _____

Does this bird chirp or sing? _____
Describe the sound: _____
_____

Is this bird a carnivore, herbivore, or omnivore? _____

If this bird migrates in the winter,
how far will it travel? _____

Describe this bird's habitat (nest, trees, woods, etc.): _____
_____
_____
_____

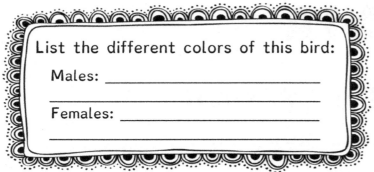

List the different colors of this bird:

Males: _____

_____

Females: _____

_____

Find this state on page **5** and use a different color to fill it in.

CREATIVE WRITING

In the space below, write a poem, short story, or a unique history tid-bit about the state bird. If this bird lives in your state, try taking a picture of the bird in its natural habitat and tape the picture to this page!

_____

_____

_____

_____

_____

_____

_____

_____

_____

What is the bird's average wingspan?

_____

What is the average weight?

_____

Which region did this bird originate?

_____

Can this bird be domesticated?

_____

List the sources you used to research this bird:

Books: _____

Websites: _____

Other sources: _____

CALIFORNIA

The state bird is:
California Valley Quail

Find the binomial name: _____

  List any nicknames for this bird: _____

Does this bird chirp or sing? _____
  Describe the sound: _____
_____

  Is this bird a carnivore, herbivore, or omnivore? _____

  If this bird migrates in the winter,
  how far will it travel? _____

Describe this bird's habitat (nest, trees, woods, etc.): _____
_____
_____
_____

Fun fact:
The California quail will travel in convoys around **40** birds but there have been reports of convoys with more than **1000** birds!

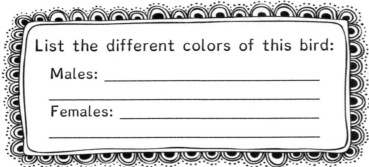

List the different colors of this bird:

Males: _____

_____

Females: _____

_____

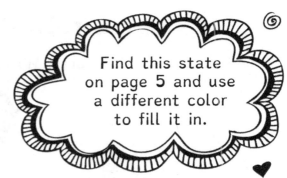

Find this state on page **5** and use a different color to fill it in.

CREATIVE WRITING

In the space below, write a poem, short story, or a unique history tid-bit about the state bird. If this bird lives in your state, try taking a picture of the bird in its natural habitat and tape the picture to this page!

_____

_____

_____

_____

_____

_____

_____

_____

What is the bird's average wingspan?

_____

What is the average weight?

_____

Which region did this bird originate?

_____

Can this bird be domesticated?

_____

List the sources you used to research this bird:

Books: _____

_____

Websites: _____

Other sources: _____

_____

CREATIVE ARTS

Fill in the missing parts. Write the name of each bird from this section:

CREATIVE ARTS

Draw your favorite bird from this section. Use your imagination to draw the bird in its natural habitat. Add a house, forest, or animals!

COLORADO

The state bird is: Lark Bunting

Find the binomial name: _____

  List any nicknames for this bird: _____

Does this bird chirp or sing? _____
  Describe the sound: _____
_____

  Is this bird a carnivore, herbivore, or omnivore? _____

  If this bird migrates in the winter,
    how far will it travel? _____

Describe this bird's habitat (nest, trees, woods, etc.): _____
_____
_____
_____

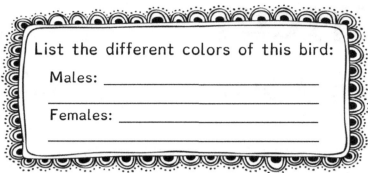

List the different colors of this bird:

Males: _____

_____

Females: _____

_____

Find this state on page 5 and use a different color to fill it in.

CREATIVE WRITING

In the space below, write a poem, short story, or a unique history tid-bit about the state bird. If this bird lives in your state, try taking a picture of the bird in its natural habitat and tape the picture to this page!

_____

_____

_____

_____

_____

_____

_____

_____

What is the bird's average wingspan?

_____

What is the average weight?

Which region did this bird originate?

_____

Can this bird be domesticated?

_____

List the sources you used to research this bird:

Books: _____

_____

Websites: _____

_____

Other sources: _____

_____

CONNECTICUT

The state bird is: **American Robin**

Find the binomial name: _____

List any nicknames for this bird: _____

Does this bird chirp or sing? _____
Describe the sound: _____
_____

Is this bird a carnivore, herbivore, or omnivore? _____

If this bird migrates in the winter,
how far will it travel? _____

Describe this bird's habitat (nest, trees, woods, etc.): _____
_____
_____
_____

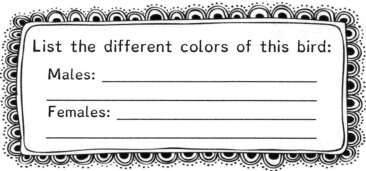

List the different colors of this bird:

Males: _____
_____

Females: _____
_____

Find this state
on page **5** and use
a different color
to fill it in.

CREATIVE WRITING

In the space below, write a poem, short story, or a unique history tid-bit about the state bird. If this bird lives in your state, try taking a picture of the bird in its natural habitat and tape the picture to this page!

_____
_____
_____
_____
_____
_____
_____
_____
_____

What is the bird's
average wingspan?

_____

What is the average weight?

_____

Which region did this
bird originate?

_____

Can this bird be
domesticated?

_____

List the sources you used to research this bird:

Books: _____

Websites: _____

Other sources: _____

DELAWARE

The state bird is: **Blue Hen Chicken**

Find the binomial name: _____

List any nicknames for this bird: _____

Does this bird chirp or sing? _____
Describe the sound: _____
_____

Is this bird a carnivore, herbivore, or omnivore? _____

If this bird migrates in the winter,
how far will it travel? _____

Describe this bird's habitat (nest, trees, woods, etc.): _____
_____
_____
_____

Fun fact:
The athletic teams at the
University of Delaware
are nicknamed the
"Fightin' Blue Hens."

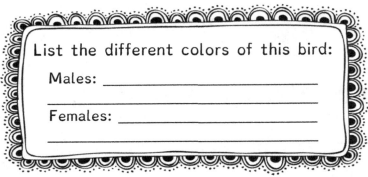

List the different colors of this bird:

Males: _____

_____

Females: _____

_____

Find this state on page **5** and use a different color to fill it in.

CREATIVE WRITING

In the space below, write a poem, short story, or a unique history tid-bit about the state bird. If this bird lives in your state, try taking a picture of the bird in its natural habitat and tape the picture to this page!

_____

_____

_____

_____

_____

_____

_____

_____

_____

_____

What is the bird's average wingspan?

_____

What is the average weight?

_____

Which region did this bird originate?

_____

Can this bird be domesticated?

_____

List the sources you used to research this bird:

Books: _____

_____

Websites: _____

_____

Other sources: _____

_____

FLORIDA

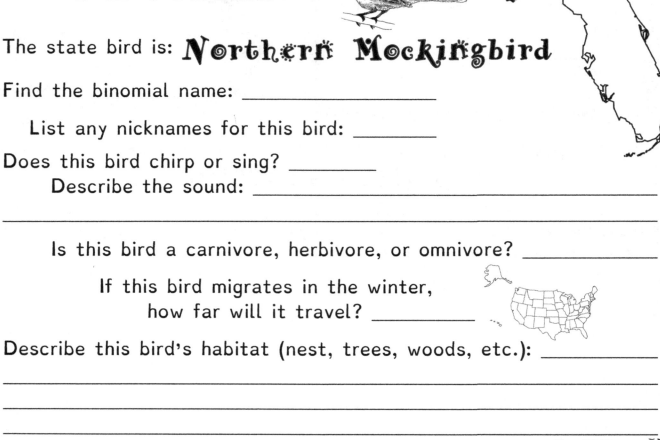

The state bird is: Northern Mockingbird

Find the binomial name: _____

   List any nicknames for this bird: _____

Does this bird chirp or sing? _____
   Describe the sound: _____
_____

   Is this bird a carnivore, herbivore, or omnivore? _____

   If this bird migrates in the winter,
      how far will it travel? _____

Describe this bird's habitat (nest, trees, woods, etc.): _____
_____
_____
_____

Fun fact:
The northern mockingbird is
known for its intelligence and
can recognize humans!

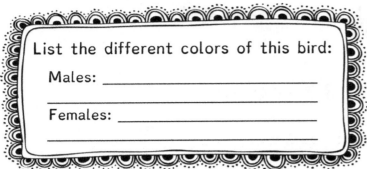

List the different colors of this bird:

Males: _____

_____

Females: _____

_____

Find this state on page 5 and use a different color to fill it in.

CREATIVE WRITING

In the space below, write a poem, short story, or a unique history tid-bit about the state bird. If this bird lives in your state, try taking a picture of the bird in its natural habitat and tape the picture to this page!

_____

_____

_____

_____

_____

_____

_____

_____

What is the bird's average wingspan?

_____

What is the average weight?

_____

Which region did this bird originate?

_____

Can this bird be domesticated?

_____

List the sources you used to research this bird:

Books: _____

Websites: _____

Other sources: _____

GEORGIA

The state bird is: **Brown Thrasher**

Find the binomial name: _____

List any nicknames for this bird: _____

Does this bird chirp or sing? _____
Describe the sound: _____
_____

Is this bird a carnivore, herbivore, or omnivore? _____

If this bird migrates in the winter,
how far will it travel? _____

Describe this bird's habitat (nest, trees, woods, etc.): _____
_____
_____
_____

Fun fact:
The male brown
thrasher has around
3,000 song
phrases!!

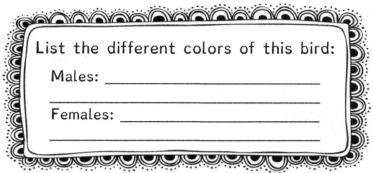

List the different colors of this bird:

Males: _____

_____

Females: _____

_____

Find this state on page 5 and use a different color to fill it in.

❋❋

CREATIVE WRITING

In the space below, write a poem, short story, or a unique history tid-bit about the state bird. If this bird lives in your state, try taking a picture of the bird in its natural habitat and tape the picture to this page!

_____

_____

_____

_____

_____

_____

_____

_____

_____

_____

❋❋

What is the bird's average wingspan?

_____

What is the average weight?

_____

Which region did this bird originate?

_____

Can this bird be domesticated?

_____

List the sources you used to research this bird:

Books: _____

_____

Websites: _____

_____

Other sources: _____

_____

CREATIVE ARTS

Fill in the missing parts. Write the name of each bird from this section:

CREATIVE ARTS

Draw your favorite bird from this section. Use your imagination to draw the bird in its natural habitat. Add a house, forest, or animals!

HAWAII

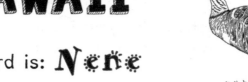

The state bird is: Nene

Find the binomial name: _____

  List any nicknames for this bird: _____

Does this bird chirp or sing? _____
  Describe the sound: _____
_____

  Is this bird a carnivore, herbivore, or omnivore? _____

  If this bird migrates in the winter,
    how far will it travel? _____

Describe this bird's habitat (nest, trees, woods, etc.): _____
_____
_____
_____

Fun fact:
The nene is endangered
and found exclusively on
the Hawaiian Islands of
Hawai'i, Maui, Moloka'i,
Kaua'i, and just recently
in O'ahu.

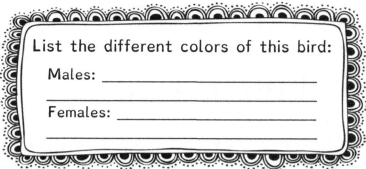

List the different colors of this bird:

Males: _____

_____

Females: _____

_____

Find this state on page 5 and use a different color to fill it in.

CREATIVE WRITING

In the space below, write a poem, short story, or a unique history tid-bit about the state bird. If this bird lives in your state, try taking a picture of the bird in its natural habitat and tape the picture to this page!

_____

_____

_____

_____

_____

_____

_____

_____

_____

_____

What is the bird's average wingspan?

_____

What is the average weight?

Which region did this bird originate?

_____

Can this bird be domesticated?

_____

List the sources you used to research this bird:

Books: _____

_____

Websites: _____

_____

Other sources: _____

_____

IDAHO

The state bird is: **Mountain Bluebird**

Find the binomial name: _____

List any nicknames for this bird: _____

Does this bird chirp or sing? _____

Describe the sound: _____

_____

Is this bird a carnivore, herbivore, or omnivore? _____

If this bird migrates in the winter,
how far will it travel? _____

Describe this bird's habitat (nest, trees, woods, etc.): _____

_____

_____

_____

What are the differences between an eastern and a mountain bluebird?

_____

_____

_____

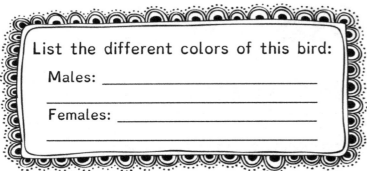

List the different colors of this bird:

Males: _____

_____

Females: _____

_____

Find this state on page **5** and use a different color to fill it in.

****

CREATIVE WRITING

In the space below, write a poem, short story, or a unique history tid-bit about the state bird. If this bird lives in your state, try taking a picture of the bird in its natural habitat and tape the picture to this page!

_____

_____

_____

_____

_____

_____

_____

_____

_____

_____

****

What is the bird's average wingspan?

_____

What is the average weight?

_____

Which is taller, the Eastern or Western White Pine?

_____

List the sources you used to research this bird:

Books: _____

_____

Websites: _____

_____

Other sources: _____

_____

ILLINOIS

The state bird is: Northern Cardinal

Find the binomial name: _____

List any nicknames for this bird: _____

Does this bird chirp or sing? _____
Describe the sound: _____
_____

Is this bird a carnivore, herbivore, or omnivore? _____

If this bird migrates in the winter,
how far will it travel? _____

Describe this bird's habitat (nest, trees, woods, etc.): _____
_____
_____
_____

List the different colors of this bird:

Males: _____

_____

Females: _____

_____

Find this state on page **5** and use a different color to fill it in.

CREATIVE WRITING

In the space below, write a poem, short story, or a unique history tid-bit about the state bird. If this bird lives in your state, try taking a picture of the bird in its natural habitat and tape the picture to this page!

_____

_____

_____

_____

_____

_____

_____

_____

_____

What is the bird's average wingspan?

_____

What is the average weight?

_____

Which region did this bird originate?

_____

Can this bird be domesticated?

_____

List the sources you used to research this bird:

Books: _____

Websites: _____

Other sources: _____

INDIANA

The state bird is: Northern Cardinal

Find the binomial name: _____

  List any nicknames for this bird: _____

Does this bird chirp or sing? _____
  Describe the sound: _____
_____

  Is this bird a carnivore, herbivore, or omnivore? _____

  If this bird migrates in the winter,
    how far will it travel? _____

Describe this bird's habitat (nest, trees, woods, etc.): _____
_____
_____
_____

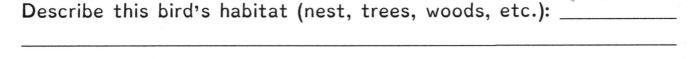

List the different colors of this bird:

Males: _____

_____

Females: _____

_____

Find this state on page 5 and use a different color to fill it in.

CREATIVE WRITING

In the space below, write a poem, short story, or a unique history tid-bit about the state bird. If this bird lives in your state, try taking a picture of the bird in its natural habitat and tape the picture to this page!

_____

_____

_____

_____

_____

_____

_____

_____

What is the bird's average wingspan?

_____

What is the average weight?

_____

Which region did this bird originate?

_____

Can this bird be domesticated?

_____

List the sources you used to research this bird:

Books: _____

Websites: _____

_____

Other sources: _____

_____

IOWA

The state bird is: Eastern Goldfinch

Find the binomial name: _____

   List any nicknames for this bird: _____

Does this bird chirp or sing? _____
   Describe the sound: _____

_____

   Is this bird a carnivore, herbivore, or omnivore? _____

   If this bird migrates in the winter,
      how far will it travel? _____

Describe this bird's habitat (nest, trees, woods, etc.): _____

_____

_____

_____

List the different colors of this bird:

Males: _____
_____

Females: _____
_____

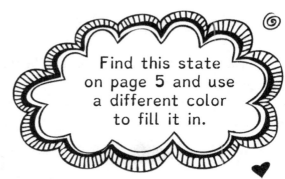

Find this state on page 5 and use a different color to fill it in.

CREATIVE WRITING

In the space below, write a poem, short story, or a unique history tid-bit about the state bird. If this bird lives in your state, try taking a picture of the bird in its natural habitat and tape the picture to this page!

_____
_____
_____
_____
_____
_____
_____
_____
_____
_____

What is the bird's average wingspan?

_____

What is the average weight?

_____

Which region did this bird originate?

_____

Can this bird be domesticated?

_____

List the sources you used to research this bird:

Books: _____
_____

Websites: _____
_____

Other sources: _____
_____

CREATIVE ARTS

Fill in the missing parts. Write the name of each bird from this section:

CREATIVE ARTS

Draw your favorite bird from this section. Use your imagination to draw the bird in its natural habitat. Add a house, forest, or animals!

KANSAS

The state bird is:

Western Meadowlark

Find the binomial name: _____

List any nicknames for this bird: _____

Does this bird chirp or sing? _____
Describe the sound: _____
_____

Is this bird a carnivore, herbivore, or omnivore? _____

If this bird migrates in the winter,
how far will it travel? _____

Describe this bird's habitat (nest, trees, woods, etc.): _____
_____
_____
_____

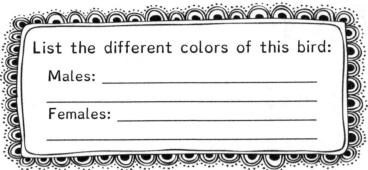

List the different colors of this bird:

Males: _____

_____

Females: _____

_____

Find this state on page **5** and use a different color to fill it in.

CREATIVE WRITING

In the space below, write a poem, short story, or a unique history tid-bit about the state bird. If this bird lives in your state, try taking a picture of the bird in its natural habitat and tape the picture to this page!

_____

_____

_____

_____

_____

_____

_____

_____

_____

_____

What is the bird's average wingspan?

_____

What is the average weight?

_____

Which region did this bird originate?

_____

Can this bird be domesticated?

_____

List the sources you used to research this bird:

Books: _____

_____

Websites: _____

_____

Other sources: _____

_____

KENTUCKY

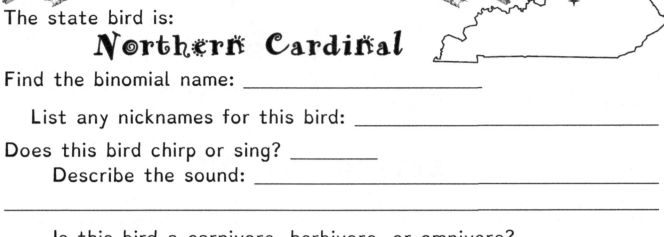

The state bird is:

Northern Cardinal

Find the binomial name: _____

List any nicknames for this bird: _____

Does this bird chirp or sing? _____
Describe the sound: _____
_____

Is this bird a carnivore, herbivore, or omnivore? _____

If this bird migrates in the winter,
how far will it travel? _____

Describe this bird's habitat (nest, trees, woods, etc.): _____
_____
_____
_____

Fun fact:
The northern cardinal rep-
resents more states (7)
than any other bird!

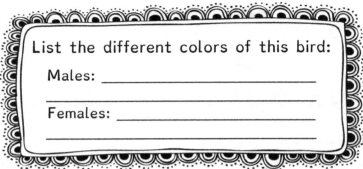

List the different colors of this bird:

Males: _____

_____

Females: _____

_____

Find this state on page **5** and use a different color to fill it in.

****

CREATIVE WRITING

In the space below, write a poem, short story, or a unique history tid-bit about the state bird. If this bird lives in your state, try taking a picture of the bird in its natural habitat and tape the picture to this page!

_____

_____

_____

_____

_____

_____

_____

_____

****

What is the bird's average wingspan?

_____

What is the average weight?

_____

Which region did this bird originate?

_____

Can this bird be domesticated?

_____

List the sources you used to research this bird:

Books: _____

_____

Websites: _____

_____

Other sources: _____

_____

LOUISIANA

The state bird is:
Eastern Brown Pelican

Find the binomial name: _____

   List any nicknames for this bird: _____

Does this bird chirp or sing? _____
   Describe the sound: _____
_____

   The brown pelican is a carnivore that feeds primarily on fish.
What is the name of this kind of mammal?

_____

Describe this bird's habitat (nest, trees, woods, etc.): _____
_____
_____
_____

Fun fact:
Of the nine species of pelicans, the brown pelican and the Peruvian pelican are the only two species that fly through the air submerging into the ocean to catch its prey.

List the different colors of this bird:

Males: _____

_____

Females: _____

_____

Find this state on page 5 and use a different color to fill it in.

CREATIVE WRITING

In the space below, write a poem, short story, or a unique history tid-bit about the state bird. If this bird lives in your state, try taking a picture of the bird in its natural habitat and tape the picture to this page!

_____

_____

_____

_____

_____

_____

_____

_____

What is the bird's average wingspan?

_____

What is the average weight?

_____

Which region did this bird originate?

_____

Can this bird be domesticated?

_____

List the sources you used to research this bird:

Books: _____

Websites: _____

_____

Other sources: _____

_____

MAINE

The state bird is: **Black-Capped Chickadee**

Find the binomial name: _____

List any nicknames for this bird: _____

Does this bird chirp or sing? _____
Describe the sound: _____
_____

Is this bird a carnivore, herbivore, or omnivore? _____

If this bird migrates in the winter,
how far will it travel? _____

Describe this bird's habitat (nest, trees, woods, etc.): _____
_____
_____
_____

Fun fact:
The chickadee is a cavity-nesting bird that excavates a new nest each season, leaving the old nest for other animals to re-use for their nest.

List the different colors of this bird:

Males: _____
_____

Females: _____
_____

Find this state on page **5** and use a different color to fill it in.

CREATIVE WRITING

In the space below, write a poem, short story, or a unique history tid-bit about the state bird. If this bird lives in your state, try taking a picture of the bird in its natural habitat and tape the picture to this page!

_____
_____
_____
_____
_____
_____
_____
_____

What is the bird's average wingspan?

_____

What is the average weight?

_____

Which region did this bird originate?

_____

Can this bird be domesticated?

_____

List the sources you used to research this bird:

Books: _____

Websites: _____
_____

Other sources: _____
_____

MARYLAND

The state bird is: **Baltimore Oriole**

Find the binomial name: _____

List any nicknames for this bird: _____

Does this bird chirp or sing? _____

Describe the sound: _____

_____

Is this bird a carnivore, herbivore, or omnivore? _____

If this bird migrates in the winter,
how far will it travel? _____

Describe this bird's habitat (nest, trees, woods, etc.): _____

_____

_____

_____

Fun fact:
Baltimore, Maryland's
major league baseball team,
The Baltimore Orioles,
was named after this bird
in 1894.

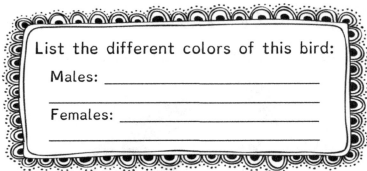

List the different colors of this bird:

Males: _____

_____

Females: _____

_____

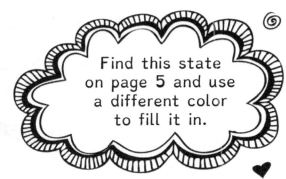

Find this state on page 5 and use a different color to fill it in.

CREATIVE WRITING

In the space below, write a poem, short story, or a unique history tid-bit about the state bird. If this bird lives in your state, try taking a picture of the bird in its natural habitat and tape the picture to this page!

_____

_____

_____

_____

_____

_____

_____

_____

_____

What is the bird's average wingspan?

_____

What is the average weight?

_____

Which region did this bird originate?

_____

Can this bird be domesticated?

_____

List the sources you used to research this bird:

Books: _____

_____

Websites: _____

_____

Other sources: _____

_____

CREATIVE ARTS

Fill in the missing parts. Write the name of each bird from this section:

CREATIVE ARTS

Draw your favorite bird from this section. Use your imagination to draw the bird in its natural habitat. Add a house, forest, or animals!

MASSACHUSETTS

The state bird is:

Black-Capped Chickadee

Find the binomial name: _____

   List any nicknames for this bird: _____

Does this bird chirp or sing? _____
   Describe the sound: _____
_____

   Is this bird a carnivore, herbivore, or omnivore? _____

   If this bird migrates in the winter,
   how far will it travel? _____

Describe this bird's habitat (nest, trees, woods, etc.): _____
_____
_____
_____

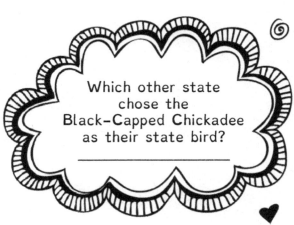

Which other state
chose the
Black-Capped Chickadee
as their state bird?

_____

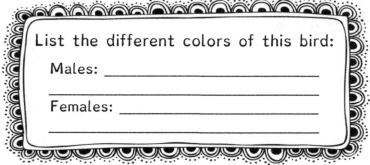

List the different colors of this bird:

Males: _____
_____

Females: _____
_____

Find this state on page 5 and use a different color to fill it in.

✳✳✳✳✳✳✳✳✳✳✳✳✳✳✳✳✳✳✳✳✳✳✳✳✳✳✳✳✳✳✳✳✳✳✳✳✳✳

CREATIVE WRITING

In the space below, write a poem, short story, or a unique history tid-bit about the state bird. If this bird lives in your state, try taking a picture of the bird in its natural habitat and tape the picture to this page!

_____
_____
_____
_____
_____
_____
_____
_____
_____
_____

✳✳✳✳✳✳✳✳✳✳✳✳✳✳✳✳✳✳✳✳✳✳✳✳✳✳✳✳✳✳✳✳✳✳✳✳✳✳

What is the bird's average wingspan?

_____

What is the average weight?

_____

Which region did this bird originate?

_____

Can this bird be domesticated?

_____

List the sources you used to research this bird:

Books: _____
_____

Websites: _____
_____

Other sources: _____
_____

MICHIGAN

The state bird is: *American Robin*

Find the binomial name: _____

   List any nicknames for this bird: _____

Does this bird chirp or sing? _____
   Describe the sound: _____
_____

   Is this bird a carnivore, herbivore, or omnivore? _____

   If this bird migrates in the winter,
     how far will it travel? _____

Describe this bird's habitat (nest, trees, woods, etc.): _____
_____
_____
_____

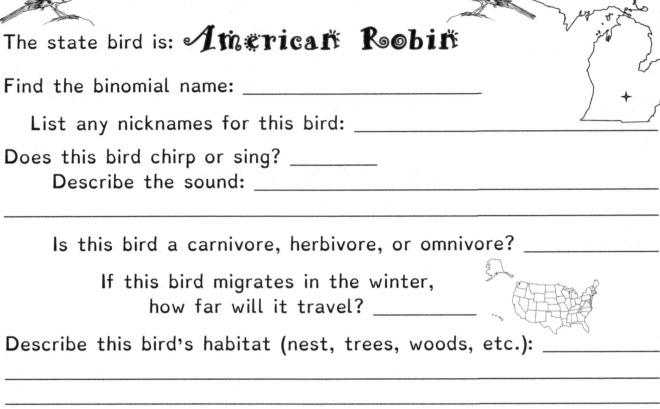

List the different colors of this bird:

Males: _____

_____

Females: _____

_____

Find this state on page 5 and use a different color to fill it in.

CREATIVE WRITING

In the space below, write a poem, short story, or a unique history tid-bit about the state bird. If this bird lives in your state, try taking a picture of the bird in its natural habitat and tape the picture to this page!

_____

_____

_____

_____

_____

_____

_____

_____

What is the bird's average wingspan?

_____

What is the average weight?

Which region did this bird originate?

_____

Can this bird be domesticated?

_____

List the sources you used to research this bird:

Books: _____

Websites: _____

Other sources: _____

MINNESOTA

The state bird is: Common Loon

Find the binomial name: _____

List any nicknames for this bird: _____

Does this bird chirp or sing? _____
Describe the sound: _____
_____

Is this bird a carnivore, herbivore, or omnivore? _____

If this bird migrates in the winter,
how far will it travel? _____

Describe this bird's habitat (nest, trees, woods, etc.): _____
_____
_____
_____

Fun fact:
Loons are extremely fast while flying
and diving. They will plunge 90 feet
underwater to catch a fish!

List the different colors of this bird:

Males: _____

_____

Females: _____

_____

Find this state on page 5 and use a different color to fill it in.

CREATIVE WRITING

In the space below, write a poem, short story, or a unique history tid-bit about the state bird. If this bird lives in your state, try taking a picture of the bird in its natural habitat and tape the picture to this page!

_____

_____

_____

_____

_____

_____

_____

_____

_____

_____

What is the bird's average wingspan?

_____

What is the average weight?

_____

Which region did this bird originate?

_____

Can this bird be domesticated?

_____

List the sources you used to research this bird:

Books: _____

_____

Websites: _____

_____

Other sources: _____

_____

MISSISSIPPI

The state bird is: **Northern Mockingbird**

Find the binomial name: _____

List any nicknames for this bird: _____

Does this bird chirp or sing? _____
Describe the sound: _____
_____

Is this bird a carnivore, herbivore, or omnivore? _____

If this bird migrates in the winter,
how far will it travel? _____

Describe this bird's habitat (nest, trees, woods, etc.): _____
_____
_____
_____

Fun fact:

The Mockingbird can sing up to 200 songs!

List the different colors of this bird:

Males: _____
_____

Females: _____
_____

Find this state on page **5** and use a different color to fill it in.

CREATIVE WRITING

In the space below, write a poem, short story, or a unique history tid-bit about the state bird. If this bird lives in your state, try taking a picture of the bird in its natural habitat and tape the picture to this page!

_____
_____
_____
_____
_____
_____
_____
_____

What is the bird's average wingspan?

_____

What is the average weight?

Which region did this bird originate?

_____

Can this bird be domesticated?

_____

List the sources you used to research this bird:

Books: _____
_____

Websites: _____
_____

Other sources: _____
_____

MISSOURI

The state bird is: **Eastern Bluebird**

Find the binomial name: _____

List any nicknames for this bird: _____

Does this bird chirp or sing? _____
Describe the sound: _____
_____

Is this bird a carnivore, herbivore, or omnivore? _____

If this bird migrates in the winter,
how far will it travel? _____

Describe this bird's habitat (nest, trees, woods, etc.): _____
_____
_____
_____

Fun fact:
The average lifespan of the eastern bluebird is 6 to 10 years. The longest on record is 10 years and 5 months!

64

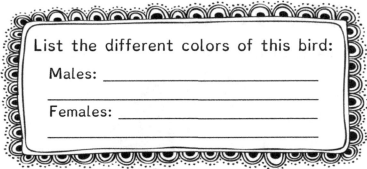

List the different colors of this bird:

Males: _____

_____

Females: _____

_____

Find this state on page **5** and use a different color to fill it in.

CREATIVE WRITING

In the space below, write a poem, short story, or a unique history tid-bit about the state bird. If this bird lives in your state, try taking a picture of the bird in its natural habitat and tape the picture to this page!

_____

_____

_____

_____

_____

_____

_____

_____

_____

_____

What is the bird's average wingspan?

_____

What is the average weight?

_____

Which region did this bird originate?

_____

Can this bird be domesticated?

_____

List the sources you used to research this bird:

Books: _____

_____

Websites: _____

_____

Other sources: _____

_____

CREATIVE ARTS

Fill in the missing parts. Write the name of each bird from this section:

CREATIVE ARTS

Draw your favorite bird from this section. Use your imagination to draw the bird in its natural habitat. Add a house, forest, or animals!

MONTANA

The state bird is:

Western Meadowlark

Find the binomial name: _____

List any nicknames for this bird: _____

Does this bird chirp or sing? _____
Describe the sound: _____
_____

Is this bird a carnivore, herbivore, or omnivore? _____

If this bird migrates in the winter,
how far will it travel? _____

Describe this bird's habitat (nest, trees, woods, etc.): _____
_____
_____
_____

List the different colors of this bird:

Males: _____

_____

Females: _____

_____

Find this state on page 5 and use a different color to fill it in.

CREATIVE WRITING

In the space below, write a poem, short story, or a unique history tid-bit about the state bird. If this bird lives in your state, try taking a picture of the bird in its natural habitat and tape the picture to this page!

_____

_____

_____

_____

_____

_____

_____

_____

_____

What is the bird's average wingspan?

_____

What is the average weight?

_____

Which region did this bird originate?

_____

Can this bird be domesticated?

_____

List the sources you used to research this bird:

Books: _____

_____

Websites: _____

_____

Other sources: _____

_____

NEBRASKA

The state bird is:

Western Meadowlark

Find the binomial name: _____

   List any nicknames for this bird: _____

Does this bird chirp or sing? _____
   Describe the sound: _____
_____

   Is this bird a carnivore, herbivore, or omnivore? _____

   If this bird migrates in the winter,
      how far will it travel? _____

Describe this bird's habitat (nest, trees, woods, etc.): _____
_____
_____
_____

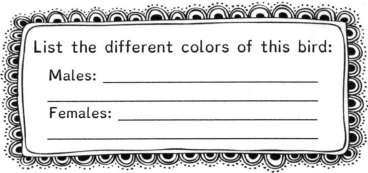

List the different colors of this bird:

Males: _____
_____

Females: _____
_____

Find this state on page **5** and use a different color to fill it in.

CREATIVE WRITING

In the space below, write a poem, short story, or a unique history tid-bit about the state bird. If this bird lives in your state, try taking a picture of the bird in its natural habitat and tape the picture to this page!

_____
_____
_____
_____
_____
_____
_____
_____
_____

What is the bird's average wingspan?

_____

What is the average weight?

_____

Which region did this bird originate?

_____

Can this bird be domesticated?

_____

List the sources you used to research this bird:

Books: _____
_____

Websites: _____
_____

Other sources: _____
_____

NEVADA

The state bird is: **Mountain Bluebird**

Find the binomial name: _____

List any nicknames for this bird: _____

Does this bird chirp or sing? _____
Describe the sound: _____
_____

Is this bird a carnivore, herbivore, or omnivore? _____

If this bird migrates in the winter,
how far will it travel? _____

Describe this bird's habitat (nest, trees, woods, etc.): _____
_____
_____
_____

Which other state
declared the
Mountain Bluebird
as their state bird?

_____

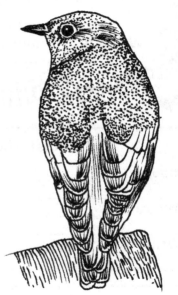

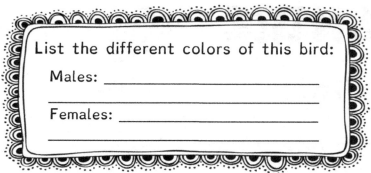

List the different colors of this bird:

Males: _____

_____

Females: _____

_____

Find this state on page 5 and use a different color to fill it in.

CREATIVE WRITING

In the space below, write a poem, short story, or a unique history tid-bit about the state bird. If this bird lives in your state, try taking a picture of the bird in its natural habitat and tape the picture to this page!

_____

_____

_____

_____

_____

_____

_____

_____

_____

What is the bird's average wingspan?

_____

What is the average weight?

_____

Which region did this bird originate?

_____

Can this bird be domesticated?

_____

List the sources you used to research this bird:

Books: _____

_____

Websites: _____

_____

Other sources: _____

_____

NEW HAMPSHIRE

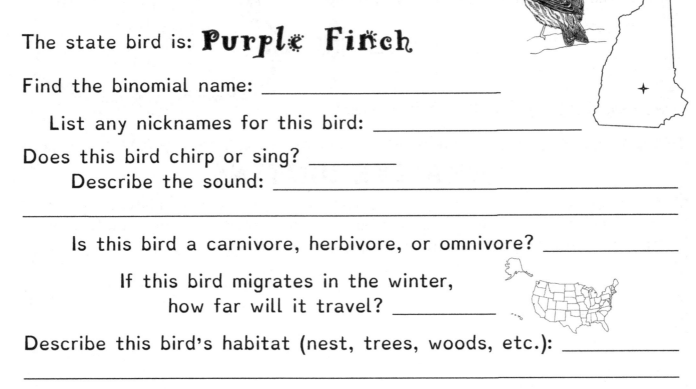

The state bird is: **Purple Finch**

Find the binomial name: _____

   List any nicknames for this bird: _____

Does this bird chirp or sing? _____
     Describe the sound: _____
_____

   Is this bird a carnivore, herbivore, or omnivore? _____

   If this bird migrates in the winter,
      how far will it travel? _____

Describe this bird's habitat (nest, trees, woods, etc.): _____
_____
_____
_____

List the different colors of this bird:

Males: _____

_____

Females: _____

_____

Find this state on page 5 and use a different color to fill it in.

CREATIVE WRITING

In the space below, write a poem, short story, or a unique history tid-bit about the state bird. If this bird lives in your state, try taking a picture of the bird in its natural habitat and tape the picture to this page!

_____

_____

_____

_____

_____

_____

_____

_____

_____

What is the bird's average wingspan?

_____

What is the average weight?

Which region did this bird originate?

_____

Can this bird be domesticated?

_____

List the sources you used to research this bird:

Books: _____

Websites: _____

Other sources: _____

_____

NEW JERSEY

The state bird is: Eastern Goldfinch

Find the binomial name: _____

  List any nicknames for this bird: _____

Does this bird chirp or sing? _____
    Describe the sound: _____
_____

  Is this bird a carnivore, herbivore, or omnivore? _____

   If this bird migrates in the winter,
     how far will it travel? _____

Describe this bird's habitat (nest, trees, woods, etc.): _____
_____
_____
_____

Fun fact:
American Goldfinches
are some of the easiest
birds to attract to
backyard bird feeders!

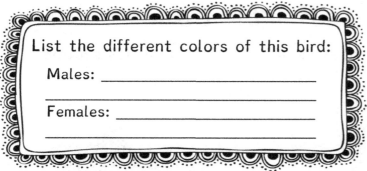

List the different colors of this bird:

Males: _____

_____

Females: _____

_____

Find this state on page 5 and use a different color to fill it in.

CREATIVE WRITING

In the space below, write a poem, short story, or a unique history tid-bit about the state bird. If this bird lives in your state, try taking a picture of the bird in its natural habitat and tape the picture to this page!

_____

_____

_____

_____

_____

_____

_____

_____

_____

_____

What is the bird's average wingspan?

_____

What is the average weight?

_____

Which region did this bird originate?

_____

Can this bird be domesticated?

_____

List the sources you used to research this bird:

Books: _____

_____

Websites: _____

_____

Other sources: _____

_____

CREATIVE ARTS

Fill in the missing parts. Write the name of each bird from this section:

CREATIVE ARTS

Draw your favorite bird from this section. Use your imagination to draw the bird in its natural habitat. Add a house, forest, or animals!

NEW MEXICO

The state bird is:

Greater Roadrunner

Find the binomial name: _____

　List any nicknames for this bird: _____

Does this bird chirp or sing? _____
　Describe the sound: _____
_____

　Is this bird a carnivore, herbivore, or omnivore? _____

　If this bird migrates in the winter,
　　how far will it travel? _____

Describe this bird's habitat (nest, trees, woods, etc.): _____
_____
_____
_____

Fun fact:
The Road Runner is a famous character of a long-running (1949) Warner Brothers cartoon series. He is famous for his vexation of Wile E. Coyote!

List the different colors of this bird:

Males: _____

_____

Females: _____

_____

Find this state on page 5 and use a different color to fill it in.

CREATIVE WRITING

In the space below, write a poem, short story, or a unique history tid-bit about the state bird. If this bird lives in your state, try taking a picture of the bird in its natural habitat and tape the picture to this page!

_____

_____

_____

_____

_____

_____

_____

_____

What is the bird's average wingspan?

_____

What is the average weight?

Which region did this bird originate?

_____

Can this bird be domesticated?

_____

List the sources you used to research this bird:

Books: _____

Websites: _____

Other sources: _____

NEW YORK

The state bird is:
Eastern Bluebird

Find the binomial name: _____

List any nicknames for this bird: _____

Does this bird chirp or sing? _____

Describe the sound: _____

_____

Is this bird a carnivore, herbivore, or omnivore? _____

If this bird migrates in the winter,
how far will it travel? _____

Describe this bird's habitat (nest, trees, woods, etc.): _____

_____

_____

_____

Which other state
declared the
Eastern Bluebird
as their state bird?

_____

List the different colors of this bird:

Males: _____

_____

Females: _____

_____

Find this state on page **5** and use a different color to fill it in.

✳ CREATIVE WRITING

In the space below, write a poem, short story, or a unique history tid-bit about the state bird. If this bird lives in your state, try taking a picture of the bird in its natural habitat and tape the picture to this page!

_____

_____

_____

_____

_____

_____

_____

_____

What is the bird's average wingspan?

_____

What is the average weight?

_____

Which region did this bird originate?

_____

Can this bird be domesticated?

_____

List the sources you used to research this bird:

Books: _____

_____

Websites: _____

_____

Other sources: _____

_____

NORTH CAROLINA

The state bird is:
Northern Cardinal

Find the binomial name: _____

List any nicknames for this bird: _____

Does this bird chirp or sing? _____

Describe the sound: _____

_____

Is this bird a carnivore, herbivore, or omnivore? _____

If this bird migrates in the winter,
how far will it travel? _____

Describe this bird's habitat (nest, trees, woods, etc.): _____

_____

_____

_____

List the different colors of this bird:

Males: _____

_____

Females: _____

_____

Find this state on page 5 and use a different color to fill it in.

CREATIVE WRITING

In the space below, write a poem, short story, or a unique history tid-bit about the state bird. If this bird lives in your state, try taking a picture of the bird in its natural habitat and tape the picture to this page!

_____

_____

_____

_____

_____

_____

_____

_____

_____

What is the bird's average wingspan?

_____

What is the average weight?

_____

Which region did this bird originate?

_____

Can this bird be domesticated?

_____

List the sources you used to research this bird:

Books: _____

Websites: _____

Other sources: _____

_____

NORTH DAKOTA

The state bird is:

Western Meadowlark

Find the binomial name: _____

   List any nicknames for this bird: _____

Does this bird chirp or sing? _____
   Describe the sound: _____
_____

   Is this bird a carnivore, herbivore, or omnivore? _____

   If this bird migrates in the winter,
      how far will it travel? _____

Describe this bird's habitat (nest, trees, woods, etc.): _____
_____
_____
_____

List the different colors of this bird:

Males: _____

_____

Females: _____

_____

Find this state on page 5 and use a different color to fill it in.

CREATIVE WRITING

In the space below, write a poem, short story, or a unique history tid-bit about the state bird. If this bird lives in your state, try taking a picture of the bird in its natural habitat and tape the picture to this page!

_____

_____

_____

_____

_____

_____

_____

_____

_____

What is the bird's average wingspan?

_____

What is the average weight?

_____

Which region did this bird originate?

_____

Can this bird be domesticated?

_____

List the sources you used to research this bird:

Books: _____

Websites: _____

Other sources: _____

OHIO

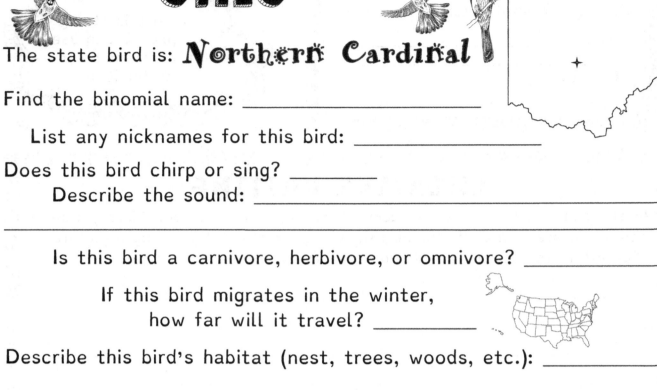

The state bird is: **Northern Cardinal**

Find the binomial name: _____

  List any nicknames for this bird: _____

Does this bird chirp or sing? _____
  Describe the sound: _____
_____

  Is this bird a carnivore, herbivore, or omnivore? _____

  If this bird migrates in the winter,
    how far will it travel? _____

Describe this bird's habitat (nest, trees, woods, etc.): _____
_____
_____
_____

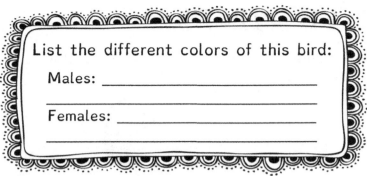

List the different colors of this bird:

Males: _____

_____

Females: _____

_____

Find this state on page 5 and use a different color to fill it in.

CREATIVE WRITING

In the space below, write a poem, short story, or a unique history tid-bit about the state bird. If this bird lives in your state, try taking a picture of the bird in its natural habitat and tape the picture to this page!

_____

_____

_____

_____

_____

_____

_____

_____

_____

_____

What is the bird's average wingspan?

_____

What is the average weight?

_____

Which region did this bird originate?

_____

Can this bird be domesticated?

_____

List the sources you used to research this bird:

Books: _____

_____

Websites: _____

_____

Other sources: _____

_____

CREATIVE ARTS

Fill in the missing parts. Write the name of each bird from this section:

CREATIVE ARTS

Draw your favorite bird from this section. Use your imagination to draw the bird in its natural habitat. Add a house, forest, or animals!

OKLAHOMA

The state bird is:
Scissor-tailed Flycatcher

Find the binomial name: _____

List any nicknames for this bird: _____

Does this bird chirp or sing? _____
Describe the sound: _____
_____

Is this bird a carnivore, herbivore, or omnivore? _____

If this bird migrates in the winter,
how far will it travel? _____

Describe this bird's habitat (nest, trees, woods, etc.): _____
_____
_____
_____

Fun fact:
Artificial (human-made) materials
make up **30%** of the weight of the
scissor-tailed flycatcher's nests,
such as paper, carpet string,
cloth, and cigarette butts! Yuck!

9

List the different colors of this bird:

Males: _____

_____

Females: _____

_____

Find this state on page 5 and use a different color to fill it in.

CREATIVE WRITING

In the space below, write a poem, short story, or a unique history tid-bit about the state bird. If this bird lives in your state, try taking a picture of the bird in its natural habitat and tape the picture to this page!

_____

_____

_____

_____

_____

_____

_____

_____

_____

What is the bird's average wingspan?

_____

What is the average weight?

_____

Which region did this bird originate?

_____

Can this bird be domesticated?

_____

List the sources you used to research this bird:

Books: _____

Websites: _____

Other sources: _____

OREGON

The state bird is:

Western Meadowlark

Find the binomial name: _____

List any nicknames for this bird: _____

Does this bird chirp or sing? _____
Describe the sound: _____
_____

Is this bird a carnivore, herbivore, or omnivore? _____

If this bird migrates in the winter,
how far will it travel? _____

Describe this bird's habitat (nest, trees, woods, etc.): _____
_____
_____
_____

9

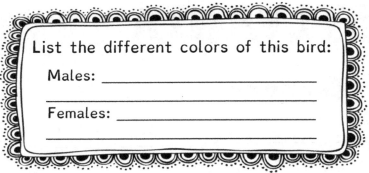

List the different colors of this bird:

Males: _____

_____

Females: _____

_____

Find this state on page **5** and use a different color to fill it in.

CREATIVE WRITING

In the space below, write a poem, short story, or a unique history tid-bit about the state bird. If this bird lives in your state, try taking a picture of the bird in its natural habitat and tape the picture to this page!

_____

_____

_____

_____

_____

_____

_____

_____

_____

What is the bird's average wingspan?

_____

What is the average weight?

_____

Which region did this bird originate?

_____

Can this bird be domesticated?

_____

List the sources you used to research this bird:

Books: _____

Websites: _____

Other sources: _____

PENNSYLVANIA

The state bird is: **Ruffed Grouse**

Find the binomial name: _____

List any nicknames for this bird: _____

Does this bird chirp or sing? _____

Describe the sound: _____

_____

Is this bird a carnivore, herbivore, or omnivore? _____

If this bird migrates in the winter,
how far will it travel? _____

Describe this bird's habitat (nest, trees, woods, etc.): _____

_____

_____

_____

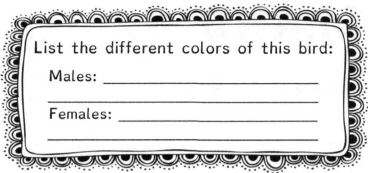

List the different colors of this bird:

Males: _____

_____

Females: _____

_____

Find this state on page 5 and use a different color to fill it in.

✳✳✳✳✳✳✳✳✳✳✳✳✳✳✳✳✳✳✳✳✳✳✳✳✳✳✳✳✳✳✳✳✳✳✳✳

CREATIVE WRITING

In the space below, write a poem, short story, or a unique history tid-bit about the state bird. If this bird lives in your state, try taking a picture of the bird in its natural habitat and tape the picture to this page!

_____

_____

_____

_____

_____

_____

_____

_____

_____

✳✳✳✳✳✳✳✳✳✳✳✳✳✳✳✳✳✳✳✳✳✳✳✳✳✳✳✳✳✳✳✳✳✳✳✳

What is the bird's average wingspan?

_____

What is the average weight?

_____

Which region did this bird originate?

_____

Can this bird be domesticated?

_____

List the sources you used to research this bird:

Books: _____

_____

Websites: _____

_____

Other sources: _____

_____

RHODE ISLAND

The state bird is: Rhode Island Red

Find the binomial name: _____

List any nicknames for this bird: _____

Does this bird chirp or sing? _____
Describe the sound: _____
_____

Is this bird a carnivore, herbivore, or omnivore? _____

If this bird migrates in the winter,
how far will it travel? _____

Describe this bird's habitat (nest, trees, woods, etc.): _____
_____
_____
_____

Which other state
declared a chicken
as their state bird?
_____

List the different colors of this bird:

Males: _____

_____

Females: _____

_____

Find this state on page **5** and use a different color to fill it in.

CREATIVE WRITING

In the space below, write a poem, short story, or a unique history tid-bit about the state bird. If this bird lives in your state, try taking a picture of the bird in its natural habitat and tape the picture to this page!

_____

_____

_____

_____

_____

_____

_____

_____

_____

What is the bird's average wingspan?

_____

What is the average weight?

Which region did this bird originate?

_____

Can this bird be domesticated?

_____

List the sources you used to research this bird:

Books: _____

_____

Websites: _____

_____

Other sources: _____

_____

SOUTH CAROLINA

The state bird is:
Great Carolina Wren

Find the binomial name: _____

List any nicknames for this bird: _____

Does this bird chirp or sing? _____

Describe the sound: _____

_____

Is this bird a carnivore, herbivore, or omnivore? _____

If this bird migrates in the winter,
how far will it travel? _____

Describe this bird's habitat (nest, trees, woods, etc.): _____

_____

_____

_____

Which other state
declared a wren
as their state bird?

_____

List the different colors of this bird:

Males: _____

_____

Females: _____

_____

Find this state on page 5 and use a different color to fill it in.

CREATIVE WRITING

In the space below, write a poem, short story, or a unique history tid-bit about the state bird. If this bird lives in your state, try taking a picture of the bird in its natural habitat and tape the picture to this page!

_____

_____

_____

_____

_____

_____

_____

_____

What is the bird's average wingspan?

_____

What is the average weight?

Which region did this bird originate?

_____

Can this bird be domesticated?

_____

List the sources you used to research this bird:

Books: _____

Websites: _____

Other sources: _____

CREATIVE ARTS

Fill in the missing parts. Write the name of each bird from this section:

CREATIVE ARTS

Draw your favorite bird from this section. Use your imagination to draw the bird in its natural habitat. Add a house, forest, or animals!

SOUTH DAKOTA

The state bird is:

Ring-necked Pheasant

Find the binomial name: _____

   List any nicknames for this bird: _____

Does this bird chirp or sing? _____
   Describe the sound: _____
_____

   Is this bird a carnivore, herbivore, or omnivore? _____

   If this bird migrates in the winter,
      how far will it travel? _____

Describe this bird's habitat (nest, trees, woods, etc.): _____
_____
_____
_____

Pheasants were
introduced into the
US during the 1880's
by which country?

_____

List the different colors of this bird:

Males: _____

_____

Females: _____

_____

Find this state on page 5 and use a different color to fill it in.

CREATIVE WRITING

In the space below, write a poem, short story, or a unique history tid-bit about the state bird. If this bird lives in your state, try taking a picture of the bird in its natural habitat and tape the picture to this page!

_____

_____

_____

_____

_____

_____

_____

_____

_____

_____

What is the bird's average wingspan?

_____

What is the average weight?

Which region did this bird originate?

_____

Can this bird be domesticated?

_____

List the sources you used to research this bird:

Books: _____

Websites: _____

Other sources: _____

TENNESSEE

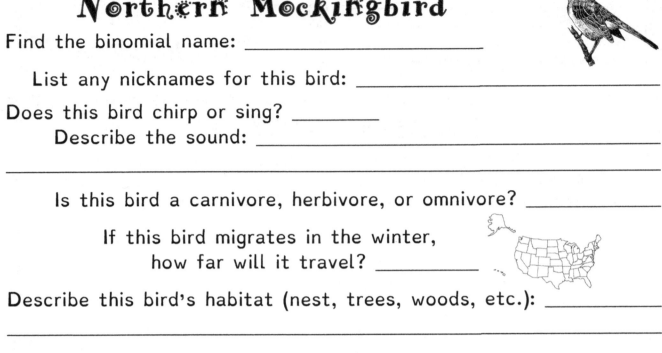

The state bird is:

Northern Mockingbird

Find the binomial name: _____

List any nicknames for this bird: _____

Does this bird chirp or sing? _____
Describe the sound: _____
_____

Is this bird a carnivore, herbivore, or omnivore? _____

If this bird migrates in the winter,
how far will it travel? _____

Describe this bird's habitat (nest, trees, woods, etc.): _____
_____
_____
_____

Fun fact:
In the wild, the northern mockingbird's lifespan is recorded to be up to **8** years, but captive birds can live up to **20** years.

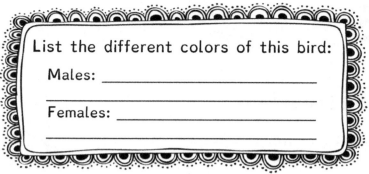

List the different colors of this bird:

Males: _____

_____

Females: _____

_____

Find this state on page **5** and use a different color to fill it in.

CREATIVE WRITING

In the space below, write a poem, short story, or a unique history tid-bit about the state bird. If this bird lives in your state, try taking a picture of the bird in its natural habitat and tape the picture to this page!

_____

_____

_____

_____

_____

_____

_____

_____

_____

_____

What is the bird's average wingspan?

_____

What is the average weight?

_____

Which region did this bird originate?

_____

Can this bird be domesticated?

_____

List the sources you used to research this bird:

Books: _____

_____

Websites: _____

Other sources: _____

_____

TEXAS

The state bird is:

Northern Mockingbird

Find the binomial name: _____

List any nicknames for this bird: _____

Does this bird chirp or sing? _____

Describe the sound: _____

_____

Is this bird a carnivore, herbivore, or omnivore? _____

If this bird migrates in the winter,
how far will it travel? _____

Describe this bird's habitat (nest, trees, woods, etc.): _____

_____

_____

_____

List the 5 states
that picked the
Northern Mockingbird
for their state bird:

_____

_____

_____

_____

_____

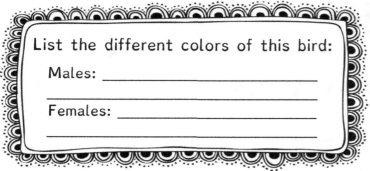

List the different colors of this bird:

Males: _____

_____

Females: _____

_____

Find this state on page 5 and use a different color to fill it in.

✳✳✳✳✳✳✳✳✳✳✳✳✳✳✳✳✳✳✳✳✳✳✳✳✳✳✳✳✳✳✳✳

CREATIVE WRITING

In the space below, write a poem, short story, or a unique history tid-bit about the state bird. If this bird lives in your state, try taking a picture of the bird in its natural habitat and tape the picture to this page!

_____

_____

_____

_____

_____

_____

_____

_____

_____

✳✳✳✳✳✳✳✳✳✳✳✳✳✳✳✳✳✳✳✳✳✳✳✳✳✳✳✳✳✳✳✳

What is the bird's average wingspan?

_____

What is the average weight?

Which region did this bird originate?

_____

Can this bird be domesticated?

_____

List the sources you used to research this bird:

Books: _____

_____

Websites: _____

_____

Other sources: _____

_____

UTAH

The state bird is: *California Gull*

Find the binomial name: _____

   List any nicknames for this bird: _____

Does this bird chirp or sing? _____
    Describe the sound: _____
_____

   Is this bird a carnivore, herbivore, or omnivore? _____

   If this bird migrates in the winter,
      how far will it travel? _____

Describe this bird's habitat (nest, trees, woods, etc.): _____
_____
_____
_____

Fun fact:
The lifespan of the
California gull is about
20 years!

11

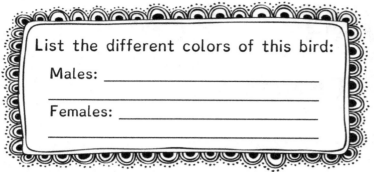

List the different colors of this bird:

Males: _____
_____
Females: _____
_____

Find this state on page **5** and use a different color to fill it in.

CREATIVE WRITING

In the space below, write a poem, short story, or a unique history tid-bit about the state bird. If this bird lives in your state, try taking a picture of the bird in its natural habitat and tape the picture to this page!

_____
_____
_____
_____
_____
_____
_____
_____
_____

What is the bird's average wingspan?

_____

What is the average weight?

_____

Which region did this bird originate?

_____

Can this bird be domesticated?

_____

List the sources you used to research this bird:

Books: _____
_____

Websites: _____
_____

Other sources: _____
_____

VERMONT

The state bird is: **Hermit Thrush**

Find the binomial name: _____

List any nicknames for this bird: _____

Does this bird chirp or sing? _____
Describe the sound: _____
_____

Is this bird a carnivore, herbivore, or omnivore? _____

If this bird migrates in the winter,
how far will it travel? _____

Describe this bird's habitat (nest, trees, woods, etc.): _____
_____
_____
_____

Interesting fact:
American poet,
Walt Whitman,
used the hermit thrush
as a symbol in his
elegy for President
Abraham Lincoln
in his famous poem,
*When Lilacs Last in the
Dooryard Bloom'd.*

List the different colors of this bird:

Males: _____
_____

Females: _____
_____

Find this state on page 5 and use a different color to fill it in.

CREATIVE WRITING

In the space below, write a poem, short story, or a unique history tid-bit about the state bird. If this bird lives in your state, try taking a picture of the bird in its natural habitat and tape the picture to this page!

_____
_____
_____
_____
_____
_____
_____
_____

What is the bird's average wingspan?

_____

What is the average weight?

_____

Which region did this bird originate?

_____

Can this bird be domesticated?

_____

List the sources you used to research this bird:

Books: _____

Websites: _____

Other sources: _____

CREATIVE ARTS

Fill in the missing parts. Write the name of each bird from this section:

CREATIVE ARTS

Draw your favorite bird from this section. Use your imagination to draw the bird in its natural habitat. Add a house, forest, or animals!

VIRGINIA

The state bird is:
Northern Cardinal

Find the binomial name: _____

   List any nicknames for this bird: _____

Does this bird chirp or sing? _____
   Describe the sound: _____
_____

   Is this bird a carnivore, herbivore, or omnivore? _____

   If this bird migrates in the winter,
      how far will it travel? _____

Describe this bird's habitat (nest, trees, woods, etc.): _____
_____
_____
_____

Fun fact:
The cardinal is the mascot
of several athletic teams,
though most teams portray
a bird with a yellow beak
and legs.

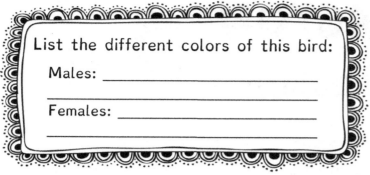

List the different colors of this bird:

Males: _____

_____

Females: _____

_____

Find this state on page 5 and use a different color to fill it in.

CREATIVE WRITING

In the space below, write a poem, short story, or a unique history tid-bit about the state bird. If this bird lives in your state, try taking a picture of the bird in its natural habitat and tape the picture to this page!

_____

_____

_____

_____

_____

_____

_____

_____

What is the bird's average wingspan?

_____

What is the average weight?

Which region did this bird originate?

_____

Can this bird be domesticated?

_____

List the sources you used to research this bird:

Books: _____

_____

Websites: _____

_____

Other sources: _____

_____

WASHINGTON

The state bird is: *Willow Goldfinch*

Find the binomial name: _____

List any nicknames for this bird: _____

Does this bird chirp or sing? _____

Describe the sound: _____

_____

Is this bird a carnivore, herbivore, or omnivore? _____

If this bird migrates in the winter,
how far will it travel? _____

Describe this bird's habitat (nest, trees, woods, etc.): _____

_____

_____

_____

Three states picked the
goldfinch for their state bird.
Name the other two states:

_____

_____

Is there a difference between
the willow goldfinch and the
eastern goldfinch? _____

11

List the different colors of this bird:

Males: _____

_____

Females: _____

_____

Find this state on page **5** and use a different color to fill it in.

***

CREATIVE WRITING

In the space below, write a poem, short story, or a unique history tid-bit about the state bird. If this bird lives in your state, try taking a picture of the bird in its natural habitat and tape the picture to this page!

_____

_____

_____

_____

_____

_____

_____

_____

_____

What is the bird's average wingspan?

_____

What is the average weight?

Which region did this bird originate?

_____

Can this bird be domesticated?

_____

List the sources you used to research this bird:

Books: _____

_____

Websites: _____

_____

Other sources: _____

_____

WEST VIRGINIA

The state bird is: Northern Cardinal

Find the binomial name: _____

List any nicknames for this bird: _____

Does this bird chirp or sing? _____
Describe the sound: _____
_____

Is this bird a carnivore, herbivore, or omnivore? _____

If this bird migrates in the winter,
how far will it travel? _____

Describe this bird's habitat (nest, trees, woods, etc.): _____
_____
_____
_____

List the 7 states
that picked the
Northern Cardinal
for their state bird:

_____
_____
_____
_____
_____
_____
_____

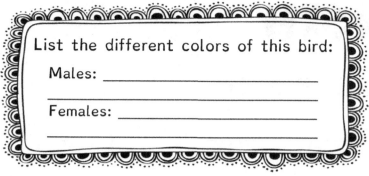

List the different colors of this bird:

Males: _____

_____

Females: _____

_____

Find this state on page **5** and use a different color to fill it in.

CREATIVE WRITING

In the space below, write a poem, short story, or a unique history tid-bit about the state bird. If this bird lives in your state, try taking a picture of the bird in its natural habitat and tape the picture to this page!

_____

_____

_____

_____

_____

_____

_____

_____

_____

What is the bird's average wingspan?

_____

What is the average weight?

Which region did this bird originate?

_____

Can this bird be domesticated?

_____

List the sources you used to research this bird:

Books: _____

_____

Websites: _____

_____

Other sources: _____

_____

WISCONSIN

The state bird is: American Robin

Find the binomial name: _____

   List any nicknames for this bird: _____

Does this bird chirp or sing? _____
   Describe the sound: _____
_____

   Is this bird a carnivore, herbivore, or omnivore? _____

   If this bird migrates in the winter,
   how far will it travel? _____

Describe this bird's habitat (nest, trees, woods, etc.): _____
_____
_____
_____

Three states declared the American Robin as their state bird. Name the other two states:

_____

_____

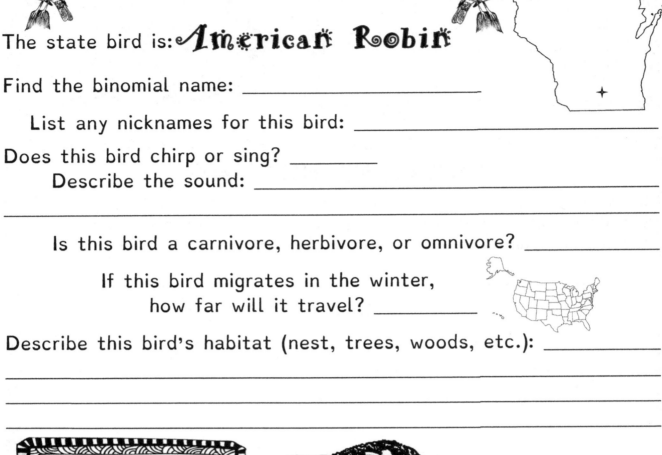

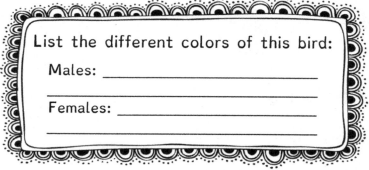

List the different colors of this bird:

Males: _____

_____

Females: _____

_____

Find this state on page 5 and use a different color to fill it in.

✻✻

CREATIVE WRITING

In the space below, write a poem, short story, or a unique history tid-bit about the state bird. If this bird lives in your state, try taking a picture of the bird in its natural habitat and tape the picture to this page!

_____

_____

_____

_____

_____

_____

_____

_____

✻✻

What is the bird's average wingspan?

_____

What is the average weight?

_____

Which region did this bird originate?

_____

Can this bird be domesticated?

_____

List the sources you used to research this bird:

Books: _____

_____

Websites: _____

_____

Other sources: _____

_____

WYOMING

The state bird is:

Western Meadowlark

Find the binomial name: _____

List any nicknames for this bird: _____

Does this bird chirp or sing? _____
Describe the sound: _____
_____

Is this bird a carnivore, herbivore, or omnivore? _____

If this bird migrates in the winter,
how far will it travel? _____

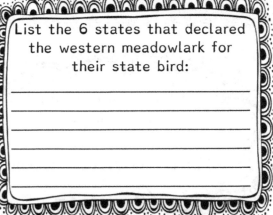

Describe this bird's habitat (nest, trees, woods, etc.): _____
_____
_____
_____

List the 6 states that declared
the western meadowlark for
their state bird:

_____
_____
_____
_____
_____

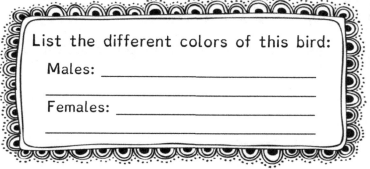

List the different colors of this bird:

Males: _____
_____

Females: _____
_____

Find this state on page **5** and use a different color to fill it in.

✳ CREATIVE WRITING

In the space below, write a poem, short story, or a unique history tid-bit about the state bird. If this bird lives in your state, try taking a picture of the bird in its natural habitat and tape the picture to this page!

_____
_____
_____
_____
_____
_____
_____
_____
_____

What is the bird's average wingspan?
_____

What is the average weight?
_____

Which region did this bird originate?
_____

Can this bird be domesticated?
_____

List the sources you used to research this bird:

Books: _____
_____

Websites: _____
_____

Other sources: _____
_____

CREATIVE ARTS

Fill in the missing parts. Write the name of each bird from this section:

CREATIVE ARTS

Draw your favorite bird from this section. Use your imagination to draw the bird in its natural habitat. Add a house, forest, or animals!

FUNSCHOOLING.COM

Made in the USA
Coppell, TX
18 May 2021